BACK TO BASICS

WITH BILLY BRAGG

BRAGG

BILLY

AVAILABLE FOR £2.99 OR LESS

7 TRACK GO! DISCS UTILITY ALBUM

LIFE'S A RIOT WITH SPY VS SPY

FROM DISCERNING RECORD SHOPS

CONTENTS

5

THE GOAT IN THE POLYTHENE BAG
BY SUSAN WILLIAMS

10

THE OFFICIAL BRAGGOGRAPHY
BY ANDY KERSHAW

14

BRAGGIGOLOGY 1982-84
FROM HULL TO ETERNITY

24

DISCOGRAPHY AND RADIO SESSIONS

26

LIFE ON THE ROAD BY BILLY

28

"I TAUGHT HIM EVERYTHING"
BY WIGGY

32

SONG INDEX

33

MUSIC

71

PHOTOGRAPHY CREDITS

72

LABOUR PARTY

© 2010 Faber Music Ltd
First published in 1985 by International Music Publications Ltd
International Music Publications Ltd is a Faber Music company
Bloomsbury House 74–77 Great Russell Street London WC1B 3DA
Printed in England by Caligraving Ltd
All rights reserved

ISBN10: 0-571-53459-7
EAN13: 978-0-571-53459-3

Dedicated with thanks to Jeff Chegwin without whom ...

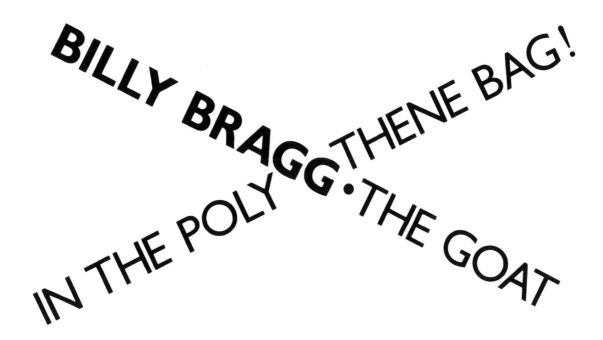

BILLY BRAGG•THE GOAT IN THE POLYTHENE BAG!

CHEEKY COCKNEY CHAPPIE BILLY BRAGG HAS TAKEN

RABID By turns both stroppy and soppy, this 6 ft. 3 inches of gristle and bone *grits* his gleaming teeth with anguish, *smashes* the strings of his cheap electric guitar with bleeding fingers and *howls* his anthems of seething sexual frustration and social concern like a mad dog with an awful tummy upset and a burning desire to destroy nastiness by singing songs about it. ● **MONSTER** The above is a load of crap, a lie, a myth, an image carefully nurtured by the shady, faceless men who manipulate the hollow manekin that is the *real* Billy Bragg!! ∇ Under the razzamattaz, the skillfully selected garments of 'street' clothing and the obviously contrived working class 'Corblimey Guv!' accent lurks a pathetic wreck, the 'man' behind the myth, the

THE WORLD OF POPULAR ENTERTAINMENT BY STORM

monster behind a million teenage screams, thousands of suicides and scores of pubescent wet-dreams. ● **DEPRAVED** William Bragg—'Wills' to his mummy and daddy—was born in a very big house to parents both disgustingly rich and depraved. After a succession of nannies he was packed off to Winchester, a very exclusive public school set in the heart of the lush green Sussex countryside. ∇ Bragg still has the school's motto, 'Thrash the Little Bastards!,' branded across his pert and perpetually clenched buttocks. Other scars are less visible, *mental* scars that would never heal, that would mark him forever as one of what Enid Blyton called 'The Legion of the Damned'—one of the foulest manifestations of the decadent and cruel British class

WITH HIS UNIQUE BRAND OF STREET-CREDIBLE ROCK 'N' ROLL.

system—the ex-public schoolboy. ● **SPAWN** Like most of the spawn of the English bourgeoisie, 1979 found our hero part of the horrific cultural maelstrom that we now know as 'New Wave.' Changing his name to Seth Twat, Bragg bought three yokels from the village workhouse and rapidly hammered them into the now legendary Poonk Rock group—'Internal 'Emmeridge' which soon had a massive repertoire of Bragg's songs under it's belt including those featured on their one and only single on Billious Braggart Records—"Let's Go De-bag Some Townies"/"Who The Flipping Heck Does The Queen Fink She Is?!?." ● **SHIT** Rock historians have yet to pinpoint the reason for the bands distinct lack of commercial success. Was it

that they failed to appreciate the growing public distaste for any group that didn't dabble in subtle sub-Carribbean polyrythmns and wear zoot-suits? Was it that they were victims of a perverted conspiracy of silence in a music press that seemed to ignore all manifestations of true working-class fury?. . . Or were they just shit? ● **DISGUST** Bragg left the group in disgust and joined the army. Much has been made of this stage in his career. Suffice to say that his stay was for only *two days* and yet he has been able to write so far, *17* songs about the experience with another *94* in the pipeline! ▽ Bragg got his marching orders from Her Majesty's Armed forces as it soon became clear that the disgusting nocturnal habits he had picked up at public school

were hardly to be tolerated in the Barrack Room. ▽ Bragg hit civvie street a pauper. His meagre savings were eaten up by the huge cost of replacing the army blankets he had so severely damaged and in 'shtum' money paid to the parents of his badly traumatised barrack-mates. ● **CRAP** The next few years were sheer hell for our Willie. People everywhere thought he was crap. Old school chums used to cross the street to avoid him and then shout rude things behind his back like—"Oh look, it's that awful Bragg cove wot never shared his tuck. I think he's *really* crap!." A far cry from today when nearly everyone has been conned into thinking that the bastard is 'a diamond geezer.' ▽ To earn a crust, Bragg turned to street busking. He stood on one leg and hummed the theme from 'Born Free' interspersed with witty cockney asides like—"Gis 10p You Tight Fisted Bastard Or I'll Kick Your Fucking Head In!" He was not a great success. ∇ He suffered from a poverty that was both physical and spiritual. He turned, in his desperation, to politics, to drugs, to organised religion and, finally, to the mod revival, all in the hope of 'finding himself,' of achieving the state of serene inner bliss described in the hallowed writings of the great Indian mystics. It fucked him up completeley. ● **FESTERING** It was a burnt-out, hollow-eyed wreck that dragged itself into the Salvation Army kitchen run by Colonel Sally Timps one bleak mid-winter's night in 1982. She tossed him a mouldy

AN APPRECIATION BY

Hovis crust and a pen, demanding that he fill in an extensive questionaire before he would be allowed to suck the moisture from the festering boil on her knee. ∇ Bragg complied, writing the words 'Rock Star' under the heading—"Previous employment and if none, why? You lazy BASTARD!!!!." Timps eye gleamed when she espied what he had written. In a flash she had leapt the counter, rabbit-punched Bragg in the kidneys and made use of the public telephone by the door. ∇ The man she phoned ws Dirk Spiegel. Spiegel was a man possessed, possessed by a mad, crazed and impossible dream. He dreamt of a society swept free of the hideous sexual ambiguity that is so prelevant in pop-music. He dreamt of a heterosexual paradise where Cliff

SUSAN WILLIAMS

Richard and Hank Marvin could strut manfully about in corduroy sweaters without anyone sniggering. A pop scene where decency, common sense and good manners were of paramount importance and nobody had long hair or wore make-up. . . well, maybe just a *little* bit of lipstick—NO! *no* lipstick *at all!* Not even the tiniest, widgiest bit round the corners. And crew-cuts! and sensible trousers! and flat shoes! ∇ To achieve this Spiegel needed a catalyst, a man the kids could respect and look up to. A man, nay, a **boy,** a virginal Sir Gallahad slung about with a carefully battered Fender, whom he could mould with the sophisticated brainwashing techniques at his disposal, into a vigorous campaigner for all that is decent, desirable and

Ms WILLIAMS HERSELF

RIGHT!!!!!

Spiegel replaced the receiver with a smile. The raw material had arrived.

On the night of 20th December 1957 a blizzard howled around the Victorian walls of Barking Hospital and hapless knots of starlings keeled off the gables into the snowdrifts. ▷ Inside the delivery room the dashing young doctor smiled soothingly at the mother and broke the news: ▷ "It's a singer songwriter, Mrs. Bragg," he announced. ▷ "Is everything alright?," she breathed. ▷ "I can't say. Let's wait for the first album," replied the doctor sagely. ▷ Twenty-five years later the infant was to record an LP that would demolish the doctor's reservations, establish the Barking Boy as a Reluctant Folk Hero, convert big noses into a commercial proposition and inadvertently inspire a youth

sub-culture. ▷ "Life's a Riot with a Spy vs. Spy," the debut mini-LP by Billy Bragg, originally released on July 1st 1983 on Charisma's Utility label, was destined to set journalists dusting off the long forgotten "Spokesman of a Generation" cliche and popularise the £6.99 jeans, the greasy hushpuppies and the Man at Millett's check shirts—essential accoutrements of Bragg chic. ▷ Up and down the country guitar bores slapped their Stratocasters and Les Pauls onto the part-exchange counters as fashion favoured the Bragg-style bargain basement Chad

Valley special. ▷ Following a photo in The Face, bewildered barbers were bombarded with requests for the Bragg bouffant. Clearly, something was going on. ▷ But what had happened between young Bill's arrival as Upwardly Mobile Teenage Crooner and his departure from the delivery room? Well let's start again. ▷ Bill left Barking Abbey Comprehensive School at the age of 16, bought his first guitar and drifted through a variety of colourful jobs: shipping clerk, bank messenger, poodle clipper, petrol pump assistant, record shop assistant and goat herd. He learnt how to hold down the basic guitar chords from life long pal and axe-hero-next-door, Wiggy. ▷ After two years of self-conscious

strumming in Billy's kitchen our heroes formed their first proper band, Riff Raff, in 1977. Long admirers of The Faces and the Stones and inspired by the energy of the Clash, Riff Raff comprised Billy 'Bonkers' Bragg on rhythm guitar and vocals, Wiggy on lead with traditional drums and bass accompaniment. The recorded output was the Chiswick EP "I Wanna Be a Cosmonaut" (released July 1978) and a clutch of best-overlooked independent singles. ▷ Riff Raff performances puzzled the patrons of pubs around London and East Anglia with the boys' well-it-was-in-tune-when-I-bought-it musicianship. The band earned its place in rock and roll mythology with its unmourned demise in 1980. "Failure to come to

terms with abject poverty" was the official reason for the split. ▷ Hipper than thou collectors have been busy recently unearthing Riff Raff's vinyl atrocities, since Bragg went Big and even Kid Jensen has been heard to casually allude to suspect familiarity with the band's material. ▷ Frustrated and disorientated after the break up of Riff Raff, Billy made the mistake of joining the army. He wanted to drive tanks but realised the day he arrived at Catterick Camp that a stint with HM Forces was not an adventure holiday of water skiing and sight-seeing. After the statutory ninety days, he bought himself out. ▷ Back in Barking Billy picked up his guitar, plugged into his amp and locked

himself away. In the Spring of 1982 he re-emerged with new songs, new ideas and new jeans and embarked on the career of lone minstrel. Lugging his guitar and amp around London by bus and tube he performed in the familiar pub venues under the name of Spy vs. Spy. ▷ Around Christmas of 1982, in a fit of seasonal goodwill, Jeff Chegwin of Chappell Music publishers gave Billy the opportunity to make demos at their Park Street Studios and it was there on February 2nd, 3rd and 4th 1983 that tracks, later to emerge as "Life's a Riot. . ." were recorded. "live" onto two track mastertape with no overdubs. ▷ This humble collection of bitter-sweet lovesongs and bile-spitting broadsides, which at the time of writing has notched up over 110,000 sales without promotion or hype, was predictably rejected by all but one of the record companies to which it was

submitted. Peter Jenner (then Creative Director of Charisma Records, now Billy's manager), recognised qualities in Billy's tape that other A & R men thought were handicaps. With a display of admirable bottle Charisma released "Life's a Riot" as a seven-track mini-LP on the Utility label on 1st July 1983. ▷ Although a few enthusiastic voices demanded recognition for the talent John Peel had described as "a valuable addition to our cultural lives," the LP spent the summer of 1983 largely unnoticed in the racks of the odd record shop. Journalist Adam Sweeting was another pioneer, hailing Billy in the Melody Maker as a "hit and run attraction," employing "deceptively robust melodies and razor-sharp earthy wit." ▷ Peel, incidentally, had broadcast a debut Bragg session of six songs on July 31st and with characteristic open-mindedness, played tracks from "Life's a Riot" for the next six months. His support, and later that of Kid Jensen, was fundamental in familiarising the public with Bragg anthems. Listeners to the Most Wonderful Human Being's Wing-Ding voted "A New England" into 7th position in the 1983 Festive Fifty. The session was repeated twice and another was recorded for Kid Jensen. (More details of these sessions elsewhere in this book).

A RATION OF PASSION

Meanwhile Charisma Records were absorbed into the Virgin empire in September 1983 and the future of the album was put in jeopardy. To the rescue came Andy McDonald, the perfectly formed, intensely able boss of GO! Discs, a former Stiff Press Officer and appalling driver. On November 11th McDonald concluded a transfer for Bragg and the Utility label to GO! Discs and the combination of Andy's legwork and Billy's tireless gigging paid off. The LP found its way into the shops and into the independent chart, reaching the number one position in the first week of 1984. Press acclaim previously a trickle turned into a deluge with the switch to the independent label. ▷ At the end of February 1984, Billy

GO! DISCS

played his first continental gig in Paris, but he was back in London before the Parisians had noticed, except for a few enthusiastic critics. ▷ A tour supporting the Style Council in March gave Billy an insight into how the other half toured. He spent nine days on a bus with Weller, Talbot and chums, playing the massive concert halls for the first time and staying in posh hotels. The experience was more like a school trip than a tour he said afterwards. ▷ Only during the recording of his second LP "Brewing Up With Billy Bragg" was there a break in the gigging. There were dates now in Germany, Holland and Norway between engagements in Preston and Hull, so Billy played them. Meantime, he

was managing to hold down a regular job as mine host at The Captain's Cabin, Haymarket, on Sunday evenings. Anyone who wanted a gig, especially solo musicians, could have one by turning up early. Queues of Bragg fans formed round the block, new talent got an audience and the door takings were split equally. When more people were turned away than had been admitted, Billy would play in the street as well. ▷ By the late Spring, he was able to take a proper tour on the road. He set off around the country with The Redskins. The final leg of the tour was again a solo effort which allowed Billy to make the crossing to Orkney from John O'Groats in a small boat and play the first rock and roll gig on the Islands. ▷ Just before he began recording "Brewing Up," he spiritually prepared himself with a weekend at the Glastonbury CND festival. This

THE GUITAR IS MIGHTIER THAN THE TEAPOT

experience doubtless stood him in good stead for his first American tour that summer, supporting Echo and The Bunnymen. From his recollections of America, it seems the events of real significance were paddling in the Pacific, visiting Elvis Presley's monstrously tasteless house and picking up $43 thrown onto the stage by an intolerant crowd during his gig in Salt Lake City. ▷ Back to Britain and reality in September. A series of Feed the Miners benefit gigs in the coalfields brought Bragg back to earth before his autumn tour with Japanese pop

← GO BILLY → MAD ← ON FRANKS → THE CONTRA 'N' HANKS ← FLOWS →

duo, the Frank Chickens, and existential redneckers, The Hank Wangford Band, The Billy Frank 'n' Hank Tour was. . .erm. . .cosmic, the contradictions in the styles so outrageous that the whole bizarre package was a tremendous success. "Frank Chickens, Billy Bragg and Hank Wangford are all on fridge of music business" Kazuko Chicken told Radio One's Newsbeat. ▷ "Brewing Up" was released in October '84 and made a spirited dash up to number sixteen in the LP chart before darting back out again. This was only to be expected, and to say there was no video or single, the performance of "Bragg 2" was satisfying. It could never be the shock that was "Life's a Riot" but the eleven-tracker of Bragg

BILLY FRANKS'N'HANKS GO MAD ON THE CONTRAFLOWS
UNIVERSITY OF EAST ANGLIA, NORWICH 5TH
LOUGHBOROUGH UNIVERSITY 6TH
COVENTRY POLYTECHNIC 10TH
SALFORD UNIVERSITY 11TH
BIRMINGHAM UNIVERSITY 12TH
ESSEX UNIVERSITY, COLCHESTER 13TH
KEYNES COLLEGE, 16TH
UNIVERSITY OF KENT, CANTERBURY 18TH
LEEDS POLYTECHNIC
QUEEN MARGARET UNION, 19TH
GLASGOW UNIVERSITY
OCTOBER
20TH DUNDEE UNIVERSITY
21ST CALEY PALAIS, EDINBURGH
22ND THE OASIS, DUMFRIES
23RD CIVIC HALL, WHITEHAVEN, CUMBRIA
24TH KEELE UNIVERSITY
25TH NEW OCEAN CLUB, CARDIFF
26TH ROYAL COURT THEATRE, LIVERPOOL
27TH VICTORIA PALACE, LONDON
THE SHOW WILL BE FOR AT LEAST THREE HOURS, AND BILLY BRAGG WILL BE FIRST ON STAGE.

originals, with embellishments from organist Kenny Craddock and trumpeter Dave "Toots" Woodhead was Billy at his best. ▷ At the time of writing, Big Nose is recording a four track EP for early '85 release. The tracks are the lump-in-the-throat "Between the Wars," "Which Side Are You On"—an updated, bastardized Pete Seeger favourite, a new version of "It Says Here" and Leon Rosselson and Roy Bailey's "World Turned Upside Down." It will probably be called the "Between the Wars EP." "Into Battle With the Art of Song" would be much more appropriate.

BETWEEN THE WARS
BILLY BRAGG

WHILST BEING SERENADED BY HER SON STEPHEN W. MRS BRAGG LOOKS ON DESPARINGLY AND WONDERS WHEN WILL HE EVER GET A PROPER JOB?

VOLVO DRIVERS: THE EXCEPTION THAT PROVES THE RULE. B. BRAGG & ANDY KERSHAW MAINTAIN THE ONLY STREET CREDIBLE VOLVO IN EXISTENCE

BRAGGIGOLOGY 19 82 FROM HULL TO ETERNITY

MARCH 4 LADBROKE HOUSE, HIGHBURY GROVE ● *SENSIBLE JERSEYS*. **MAY 5** UPSTAIRS AT RONNIE SCOTT ● *SENSIBLE*

JERSEYS. **MAY 13** THE BRIDGEHOUSE, CANNING TOWN, TALENT CONTEST. *WON!* **JUNE 6** THE ROCK GARDEN, COVENT GARDEN

ADMIT ONE. **JULY 10** THE BRIDGEHOUSE, CANNING TOWN, TALENT CONTEST. *WON AGAIN*. **JULY 26** THE BRIDEGHOUSE AGAIN,

TALENT CONTEST FINALS: CAME SECOND! **AUGUST 14** THE SHIP, PLUMSTEAD. **SEPTEMBER 30** THE TUNNEL, GREENWICH ● *THE*

STOMPING PONDFROGS. **OCTOBER 2** SOMEWHERE IN REDHILL ● *THE STOMPING PONDFROGS*. **OCTOBER 5** THE TUNNEL,

GREENWICH ● *THE ESCAPE*. **OCTOBER 12** THE TUNNEL, GREENWICH ● *THE DANCING COUNTERPARTS*. **OCTOBER 19** THE

TUNNEL, GREENWICH ● *DOLL BY DOLL*. **OCTOBER 26** THE TUNNEL, GREENWICH ● *TIMEDANCE*. **NOVEMBER 2** THE TUNNEL,

GREENWICH ● *T34*. **NOVEMBER 3** THE LATCHMERE, BATTERSEA. **NOVEMBER 9** THE TUNNEL, GREENWICH ● *TRUE LIFE CONFES-

SIONS*. **NOVEMBER 12** THE TUNNEL, GREENWICH ● *FORTUNE*. **NOVEMBER 16** THE TUNNEL, GREENWICH ● *BLOOD AND ROSES*.

NOVEMBER 23 THE TUNNEL, GREENWICH ● *DOCTOR & THE MEDICS*. **NOVEMBER 24** THE LATCHMERE, BATTERSEA. **NOVEMBER**

30 THE TUNNEL, GREENWICH ● *RITUAL*. **DECEMBER 7** THE TUNNEL, GREENWICH ● *WIPE OUT, THE CREATURES*. **DECEMBER 14** THE

TUNNEL, GREENWICH ● *TRUE LIFE CONFESSIONS*. **DECEMBER 17** THE TUNNEL, GREENWICH ● *PAGAN ALTAR*. **DECEMBER 18** THE

GREEN MAN, STRATFORD ● *CRIME OF PASSION*. **DECEMBER 21** THE TUNNEL, GREENWICH ● *ORE*. **DECEMBER 23** THE TUNNEL,

GREENWICH ● *FORTUNE*. **DECEMBER 27** WOOLWICH TRAMSHED ● *ORSON WELLES, THE ESCORTS*.

Symbols AFTER venues denotes bands that Billy supported. NO symbol means he played solo.

BRAGGIGOLOGY 19 83 FROM HULL TO ETERNITY

JANUARY 11 THE TUNNEL, GREENWICH ■ *TONY McPHEE.* **JANUARY 18** THE TUNNEL, GREENWICH ■ *MOTION LOTION.*

JANUARY 25 THE TUNNEL, GREENWICH ■ *FRANKIE & THE FLAMES* **JANUARY 26** THE AD LIB, HOLLAND PARK. **FEBRUARY 1** THE TUNNEL, GREENWICH ■ *SHARK, TABOO.* **FEBRUARY 9** THE LATCHMERE, BATTERSEA. **FEBRUARY 23** THE LATCHMERE, BATTERSEA.

MARCH 8 THE LATCHMERE, BATTERSEA. **MARCH 10** THE AD LIB, HOLLAND PARK ■ *THE GYMSLIPS.* **MARCH 16** THE MOONLIGHT, WEST HAMPSTEAD. **MARCH 25** THE MARQUEE, WARDOUR STREET ■ *KEVIN COYNE.* **APRIL 23** THE AD LIB, HOLLAND PARK ■ *BLACKFOOT SUE.* **APRIL 29** THE WAREHOUSE, LIVERPOOL ■ *THE SINATRAS.* **APRIL 30** THE GALLERY, MANCHESTER ■ *THE SINATRAS.* **MAY 1** THE WAREHOUSE, LIVERPOOL ■ *DAVE CEE'S BIRTHDAY.* **MAY 13** THE ROEBUCK, TOTTENHAM COURT ROAD ■ *HONEST.* **MAY 14** THE GOLDEN LION, FULHAM ■ *RICKY COOL.* **MAY 17** THE ROCK GARDEN, COVENT GARDEN. **JUNE 4** THE GREYHOUND, FULHAM ■ *OPPOSITION.* **JUNE 12** THE KEY THEATRE, PETERBOROUGH. **JUNE 12** THE TOWNGATE CENTRE, BASILDON ■ *INCANTATIONS.* **JUNE 13** BAND ON THE WALL, MANCHESTER ■ *PORCH PARTY.* **JUNE 18** HATFIELD FORUM ■ *INCANTATIONS.* **JUNE 19** THEATRE ROYAL, PLYMOUTH ■ *INCANTATIONS.* **JUNE 23** THE VENUE, LIVERPOOL ■ *THE CHERRY BOYS.*

JULY 2 THE GALLERY, MANCHESTER ■ *YARGO.* **JULY 9** THE PIMLICO FESTIVAL, PIMLICO. **JULY 14** THE ROCK GARDEN, COVENT GARDEN ■ *ICICLE WORKS.* **JULY 20** THE VENUE, LIVERPOOL ■ *ICICLE WORKS.* **JULY 24** THE KEY THEATRE, PETERBOROUGH. **JULY 28** THE PEGASUS, STOKE NEWINGTON ■ *HANK WANGFORD BAND.* **AUGUST 2** NEW MERLIN'S CAVE, KING'S CROSS ■ *OPPOSITION.*

AUGUST 8 BULL & GATE, KENTISH TOWN ■ *OPPOSITION.* **AUGUST 9** THE AD LIB, HOLLAND PARK ■ *CARMEN ROLLERS.* **AUGUST 13** THE CLARENDON, HAMMERSMITH ■ *OPPOSITION.* **AUGUST 16** NEW MERLIN'S CAVE, KING'S CROSS. **AUGUST 19** THEATRE WORKSHOP BAR, EDINBURGH. **AUGUST 20** THEATRE WORKSHOP BAR, EDINBURGH. **AUGUST 22** CAFE GRAFFITI, EDINBURGH. **AUGUST 23** CAFE GRAFFITI, EDINBURGH. **AUGUST 24** THEATRE WORKSHOP BAR, EDINBURGH. **AUGUST 25** THE CIRCUIT, EDINBURGH. **AUGUST 26** THEATRE WORKSHOP BAR, EDINBURGH. **AUGUST 30** PENWITH FESTIVAL, PENZANCE ■ *MEATLOAF, CHUCK BERRY, 10CC.* **SEPTEMBER 2** THEATRE WORKSHOP BAR, EDINBURGH. **SEPTEMBER 4** CLUB MANIFESTO, EDINBURGH. **SEPTEMBER 7** THEATRE WORKSHOP BAR, EDINBURGH. **SEPTEMBER 9** THEATRE WORKSHOP BAR, EDINBURGH. **SEPTEMBER 17** THE FIFTH FUTURAMA FESTIVAL, LEEDS ■ *BAY CITY ROLLERS.* **SEPTEMBER 21** THE VENUE, LIVERPOOL ■ *VIRGIN DANCE.* **SEPTEMBER 28** ASSEMBLY HALL, STOKE NEWINGTON ■ *FLYING PICKETS.* **SEPTEMBER 28** PEGASUS, STOKE NEWINGTON ■ *OPPOSITION.* **SEPTEMBER 30** THE GREYHOUND, FULHAM ■ *OPPOSITION.* **OCTOBER 1** CITY VARIETIES, LEEDS. **OCTOBER 2** THE GROVE INN, LEEDS.

OCTOBER 6 BULL & GATE, KENTISH TOWN ■ *OPPOSITION.* **OCTOBER 7** THE CITY UNIVERSITY, NORTH LONDON ■ *OPPOSITION.* **OCTOBER 8** THE HALF MOON, HERNE HILL ■ *OPPOSITION.* **OCTOBER 9** THE ROYAL COURT, LIVERPOOL. **OCTOBER 11** THE GUILDHALL, PORTSMOUTH ■ *ROMAN HOLIDAY.* **OCTOBER 12** THE MARQUEE, WARDOUR STREET ■ *OPPOSITION.* **OCTOBER 14** HOLLOWAY COLLEGE, SURREY **OCTOBER 15** THE MARQUEE, WARDOUR STREET ■ *WENDY & THE ROCKETS.* **OCTOBER 25** READING UNIVERSITY ■ *DILLINGER.* **OCTOBER 27** SHELLEY'S CLUB, BENTON ■ *KING KURT.* **OCTOBER 29** MANCHESTER UNIVERSITY ■ *ATTILA THE STOCKBROKER.* **OCTOBER 29** MANCHESTER POLYTECHNIC ■ *SOUTHERN DEATH CULT.* **OCTOBER 30** THE KEY THEATRE,

PETERBOROUGH. **NOVEMBER 3** HENRY AFRICA'S, GLASGOW ◆ *ICICLE WORKS.* **NOVEMBER 4** EDINBURGH UNIVERSITY ◆ *ICICLE WORKS.* **NOVEMBER 5** HAVELOCK HALL, NEWCASTLE. **NOVEMBER 6** TIFFANY'S, LEEDS ■ *NEW MODEL ARMY.* **NOVEMBER 9** ALBANY, DEPTFORD ■ *RICHARD THOMPSON BAND.* **NOVEMBER 10** THE VENUE, VICTORIA ■ *RICHARD THOMPSON BAND.* **NOVEMBER 11** LEICESTER UNIVERSITY ■ *RICHARD THOMPSON BAND.* **NOVEMBER 12** THE GENERAL WOLFE, COVENTRY ◆ *ICICLE WORKS.* **NOVEMBER 14** THE MARQUEE, WARDOUR STREET ■ *NEW MODEL ARMY.* **NOVEMBER 16** THE ROCK GARDEN, COVENT GARDEN. ◆ SUPPORTING *ICICLE WORKS* AT, **NOVEMBER 17** THE HACIENDA, MANCHESTER. ◆ **NOVEMBER 18** SHEFFIELD POLYTECHNIC. ◆ **NOVEMBER 19** POLYTECHNIC OF WALES, TREFOREST. ◆ **NOVEMBER 22** LIVERPOOL UNIVERSITY. ◆ **NOVEMBER 24** MIDDLESEX POLYTECHNIC. ◆ **NOVEMBER 25** UNIVERSITY OF LONDON UNION. ◆ **NOVEMBER 26** PORTSMOUTH POLYTECHNIC. ◆ **NOVEMBER 29** LEEDS UNIVERSITY ■ *OPPOSITION.* **DECEMBER 5** EXETER UNIVERSITY ■ *SLADE.* **DECEMBER 6** READING UNIVERSITY. **DECEMBER 8** WARWICK UNIVERSITY ■ *ALVIN STARDUST.* **DECEMBER 9** QUEEN ELIZABETH COLLEGE ■ *AMAZULU.* **DECEMBER 9** MIDDLESEX POLYTECHNIC ■ *CLINT EASTWOOD & GENERAL SAINT.* **DECEMBER 10** LIVERPOOL POLYTECHNIC ◆ *ICICLE WORKS.* **DECEMBER 12** HALF MOON, HERNE HILL ■ *OPPOSITION.* **DECEMBER 13** 100 CLUB, OXFORD STREET ■ *OPPOSITION.* **DECEMBER 15** MANCHESTER UNIVERSITY ■ *DR. FEELGOOD.* **DECEMBER 16** TIN CAN CLUB, BIRMINGHAM ■ *NEW MODEL ARMY.* **DECEMBER 22** NME PARTY.

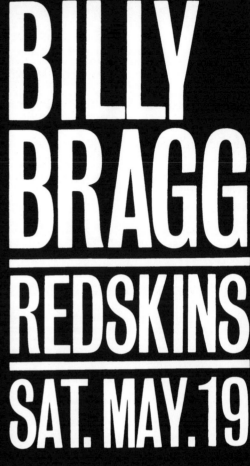

BILLY BRAGG
REDSKINS
SAT. MAY. 19

Tickets £2·50 in adv.
£3·00 on door
available from M P S U shop
and Piccaddilly Records.
MEMBERS NOTICE ! OVER 18's ONLY

POLY
9 9 OXFORD RD

BRAGGIGOLOGY 19 84 FROM HULL TO ETERNITY

JANUARY 5 ICA, THE MALL ● *REDSKINS, BRONSKI BEAT.* **JANUARY 7** THE ROEBUCK, TOTTENHAM COURT ROAD. **JANUARY 19** HATFIELD POLYTECHNIC. **JANUARY 20** N.E. LONDON POLYTECHNIC, STRATFORD ● *REDSKINS.* **JANUARY 23** KENT UNIVERSITY, CANTERBURY. **JANUARY 24** CASTAWAYS, REDHILL ● *OPPOSITION.* **JANUARY 25** PINK ELEPHANT, LUTON ● *THE THREE JOHNS.* **JANUARY 28** MANCHESTER POLYTECHNIC. **JANUARY 29** THE CAPTAIN'S CABIN, NORRIS STREET, LONDON. **JANUARY 31** KINGSTON POLYTECHNIC. **FEBRUARY 2** AYLESBURY CIVIC CENTRE. **FEBRUARY 3** SHEFFIELD POLYTECHNIC. **FEBRUARY 5** THE CAPTAIN'S CABIN, NORRIS STREET, LONDON. **FEBRUARY 9** WESTFIELD COLLEGE ● *THE BANKROBBERS.* **FEBRUARY 10** ST. CATHERINE'S COLLEGE, OXFORD. **FEBRUARY 11** RUMOURS, HASTINGS. **FEBRUARY 12** THE LYCEUM, THE STRAND ● *THE REDSKINS, THE SMITHS.* **FEBRUARY 13** COLSTON HALL, BRISTOL ● *THE CLASH.* **FEBRUARY 17** SPRING STREET THEATRE, HULL. **FEBRUARY 18** CITY LIMITS, CAMBRIDGE. **FEBRUARY 19** THE CAPTAIN'S CABIN, NORRIS STREET, LONDON. **FEBRUARY 22** THE GARAGE, NOTTINGHAM. **FEBRUARY 23** CLOUDS, PRESTON ● *THE THREE JOHNS, NEW MODEL ARMY.* **FEBRUARY 24** SHEFFIELD CITY HALL.

FEBRUARY 26 THE CAPTAIN'S CABIN, NORRIS STREET, LONDON. **FEBRUARY 29** FORUM DES HALLES, PARIS ● *OPPOSITION.* **MARCH 1** FORUM DES HALLES, PARIS ● *OPPOSITION.* **MARCH 3** QUEEN'S UNIVERSITY, BELFAST ● *REDSKINS.* **MARCH 8** SUSSEX UNIVERSITY, BRIGHTON. **MARCH 9** TRENT POLYTECHNIC, NOTTINGHAM. **MARCH 10** NATIONAL UNION STUDENTS MARCH, BATTERSEA PARK. **MARCH 10** THE ROUNDHOUSE, DAGENHAM/▼ SUPPORTING *STYLE COUNCIL* AT. **MARCH 13** GAUMONT, SOUTHAMPTON. ▼ **MARCH 14** THE DOMINION, TOTTENHAM COURT ROAD. ▼ **MARCH 15** THE DOMINION, TOTTENHAM COURT ROAD. ▼ **MARCH 16** ODEON, BIRMINGHAM. ▼ **MARCH 17** GAUMONT, IPSWICH. ▼ **MARCH 18** ROYAL CENTRE, NOTTINGHAM. ▼ **MARCH 19** CITY HALL, NEWCASTLE. ▼ **MARCH 20** APOLLO, GLASGOW. ▼ **MARCH 21** HUDDERSFIELD POLYTECHNIC. **MARCH 24** CLUB HULEN, BERGEN, NORWAY. **MARCH 25** THE CAPTAIN'S CABIN, NORRIS STREET, LONDON. **MARCH 30** TOWN HALL, ILFORD, ESSEX. **MARCH 31** THE NATIONAL STADIUM, DUBLIN ● *DAVE GILMOUR.* **APRIL 1** THE SHAW THEATRE, CAMDEN TOWN. **APRIL 5** TRADE UNION HALL, WATFORD ● *REDSKINS.* **APRIL 6** ACKLAM HALL, LADBROKE GROVE ● *REDSKINS.* **APRIL 7** BISHOP DOUGLAS SCHOOL, EAST FINCHLEY. **APRIL 8** BOURGES FESTIVAL, FRANCE. **APRIL 24** NIJMEGEN, HOLLAND ● *THE SOUND.* **APRIL 25** MILKWEG,

BRAGGIGOLOGY 19 84 FROM HULL TO ETERNITY

AMSTERDAM. **APRIL 26** VERA CLUB, GRONINGEN, HOLLAND. **APRIL 27** DE EFFENAAR, EINDHOVEN, HOLLAND. **APRIL 29**

HAMMERSMITH ODEON ● *DAVE GILMOUR*. **APRIL 30** HAMMERSMITH ODEON ● *DAVE GILMOUR*. **MAY 2** LONDON SCHOOL OF

ECONOMICS, ALDWYCH. **MAY 4** FLEET CENTRE, PETERBOROUGH./✱ WITH *THE REDSKINS* AT; **MAY 10** ELECTRIC BALLROOM,

CAMDEN. ✱ **MAY 12** PORTSMOUTH POLYTECHNIC. ✱ **MAY 15** LEICESTER UNIVERSITY. ✱ **MAY 16** PENNIES, NORWICH. ✱ **MAY 18**

NIGHT MOVES, GLASGOW. ✱ **MAY 19** MANCHESTER POLYTECHNIC. ✱ **MAY 20** MANCHESTER FREE TRADE HALL. **MAY 24** GLC

PETITION DAY, SOUTHBANK. **MAY 26** CHELTENHAM TRADE UNION DAY OF ACTION. **JUNE 2** LEEDS POLYTECHNIC *WITH REDSKINS,*

SURFIN DAVE. **JUNE 3** BREWERY ARTS CENTRE, KENDAL, CUMBRIA *WITH SURFIN DAVE.* **JUNE 4** CALEY PALAIS, EDINBURGH. **JUNE 5**

DANCE FACTORY, DUNDEE. **JUNE 6** UPSTAIRS AT THE RITZY, ABERDEEN. **JUNE 7** THE ALBERT HOTEL, KIRKWALL, ORKNEY. **JUNE 8**

PHAROAHS DISCO, INVERNESS. **JUNE 10** GLC JOBS FOR A CHANGE FESTIVAL, SOUTHBANK. **JUNE 11** PINK POP FESTIVAL, GELEEN,

HOLLAND. **JUNE 16** TRINITY HALL, BRISTOL *WITH REDSKINS.* **JUNE 17** KEY THEATRE, PETERBOROUGH. **JUNE 22** GLASTONBURY CND

FESTIVAL. **JULY 1** UNCLE POE'S HAMBURG. **JULY 2** MUSIK CONVOY, COLOGNE. **JULY 4** MALLEMUNT FESTIVAL, BRUSSELS, BELGIUM.

JULY 6 ANDY McDONALD'S WEDDING, LONDON. **JULY 7** TOURHOUT FESTIVAL, BELGIUM ● *LOU REED.* **JULY 8** ST. WENDELL'S

FESTIVAL, GERMANY ● *MARILLION.* **JULY 15** KIRKBY STADIUM, LIVERPOOL. **AUGUST 6** IRVING PLAZA, NEW YORK ● *SISTERS OF*

MERCY. **AUGUST 9, 10, 11, 12** DANCETERIA, NEW YORK CITY./✱ SUPPORTING *ECHO & THE BUNNYMEN* AT; **AUGUST 16** ONTARIO

THEATRE, WASHINGTON, D.C. ✱ **AUGUST 17** AGORA BALLROOM, HARTFORD, CONN. ✱ **AUGUST 18** OPERA HOUSE, BOSTON,

MASS. ✱ **AUGUST 19** BEACON THEATRE, NEW YORK CITY. ✱ **AUGUST 20** BEACON THEATRE, NEW YORK CITY. ✱ **AUGUST 22** LE

SPECTRUM, MONTREAL, CANADA. ✱ **AUGUST 23** INTERNATIONAL CENTRE, TORONTO, CANADA. ✱ **AUGUST 24** ROYAL OAK

THEATRE, DETROIT, MICH. ✱ **AUGUST 25** BISMARCK THEATRE, CHICAGO, ILL. ✱ **AUGUST 28** RIVERBOAT PRESIDENT, NEW

ORLEANS, LA. ✱ **AUGUST 30** CULLAN AUDITORIUM, HOUSTON, TEX. ✱ **AUGUST 31** OPRY HOUSE, AUSTIN, TEX. ✱ **SEPTEMBER 1**

BRONCO BOWL, DALLAS, TEX. ✱ **SEPTEMBER 3** MARDI GRAS, DENVER, COLO. ✱ **SEPTEMBER 5** UNIVERSITY OF UTAH,

SALT LAKE CITY. ✱ **SEPTEMBER 7** COMMUNITY CENTRE, BERKELEY, CALIF. ✱ **SEPTEMBER 8** IRVINE MEADOWS, IRVINE, CALIF. ✱

SEPTEMBER 9 GREEK THEATRE, LOS ANGELES, CALIF. ✱ **SEPTEMBER 14** PORCHESTER HALL, LONDON. **SEPTEMBER 21** PANDORA'S

BOX FESTIVAL, ROTTERDAM, HOLLAND. **SEPTEMBER 22** BEURSSCHOUWBURG, BRUSSELS, BELGIUM. **SEPTEMBER 23** VERA CLUB,

GRONINGEN. **SEPTEMBER 24** MAZZO, AMSTERDAM. **SEPTEMBER 25** HAMMERSMITH PALAIS ✱ *ECHO & THE BUNNYMEN.* SEPTEM-

BER **26** DOCKS CLUB, NEWPORT, GWENT. **SEPTEMBER 27** CIVIC HALL, CORBY, NORTHANTS. **SEPTEMBER 28** THE BUNKER,

SUNDERLAND./◆ WITH *HANK WANGFORD BAND* AND *FRANK CHICKENS* AT; **OCTOBER 5** UNIVERSITY OF EAST ANGLIA,

Symbols AFTER venues denotes bands that Billy supported.; NO symbol means he played solo.

CORBY MINERS
SUPPORT
GROUP
PRESENTS
BILLY
BRAGG
plus Interactive DISCO NEW WORLD
IMMIGRANTS
THURS. 27th SEPTEMBER 7·30pm
Willow Room   Civic Centre
Tickets £2·50 - £3 on door   All proceeds to
available from Discovery   striking miners
Bookplace

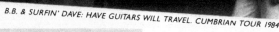

B.B. & SURFIN' DAVE: HAVE GUITARS WILL TRAVEL. CUMBRIAN TOUR 1984

THE ROAD GOES ON FOREVER

SINCERE MANAGEMENT

Ox Dist TUC Miners Support Group
CHILDRENS CHRISTMAS FUND
BENEFIT
BILLY BRAGG
JANE GOES SHOPPING   MOSES AND THE TABLETS
Sat 24th Nov.
Ox. Coll. of Further Ed.   7·11.00pm
Oxpens Rd. Oxford
All Tickets
£2.50
Ox 246318
Ox 724317

Presented by
OCFESU & Ox Dist TUC Miners Support Group

"WHEN I GET BORED I COUNT THE HEADS"

SENSITIVE GO! DISCS SUPREMO ANDY McDONALD

PULLS OFF ANOTHER AMAZING P.R. COUP

DOING THE 'GREEN BANANA' WITH THE FRANKS 'N' HANKS

BRAGGIGOLOGY 19 84 FROM HULL TO ETERNITY

NORWICH. ◆ **OCTOBER 6** LOUGHBOROUGH UNIVERSITY. ◆ **OCTOBER 7** ALDWYCH THEATRE, NCCL BENEFIT. **OCTOBER 9** THE WAG CLUB, WARDOUR STREET. **OCTOBER 10** COVENTRY POLYTECHNIC. ◆ **OCTOBER 11** SALFORD UNIVERSITY. ◆ **OCTOBER 12** BIRMINGHAM UNIVERSITY. ◆ **OCTOBER 13** ESSEX UNIVERSITY, COLCHESTER. ◆ **OCTOBER 16** KENT UNIVERSITY, CANTER-BURY. ◆ **OCTOBER 17** PARIS THEATRE, REGENT STREET, IN CONCERT BBC RADIO 1. **OCTOBER 18** LEEDS POLYTECHNIC.**OC-TOBER 19** GLASGOW POLYTECHNIC. ◆ **OCTOBER 20** DUNDEE POLYTECHNIC. ◆ **OCTOBER 21** EDINBURGH POLYTECHNIC.**OC-TOBER 22** THE OASIS, DUMFRIES. ◆ **OCTOBER 23** CIVIC HALL, WHITEHAVEN. ◆ **OCTOBER 24** KEELE UNIVERSITY. ◆ **OCTOBER 25** NEW OCEAN CLUB, CARDIFF. ◆ **OCTOBER 26** ROYAL COURT THEATRE, LIVERPOOL. ◆ **OCTOBER 27** VICTORIA PALACE, LONDON. ◆ **OCTOBER 30** ULSTER POLYTECHNIC, BELFAST. **NOVEMBER 1** THE CASTLE, GALWAY, EIRE. **NOVEMBER 2** TV CLUB, DUBLIN. **NOVEMBER 24** OXFORD COLLEGE OF FURTHER EDUCATION. **DECEMBER 4** BATSCHKAPP, FRANKFURT. **DECEMBER 5** ONKEL POES,

HAMBURG. **DECEMBER 6** THE LOFT, BERLIN. **DECEMBER 7** SCHAUBERG, BREMEN. **DECEMBER 8** ROCK MEGASENET, OREBRO, SWEDEN. **DECEMBER 9** KOLINGSBORG, STOCKHOLM. **DECEMBER 10** CLUB 77, HELSINKI, FINLAND. **DECEMBER 11** IBKIVI, JYVASKYALA, FINLAND. **DECEMBER 14** SALLEBRUN, METZ, FRANCE. **DECEMBER 16** FORUM DES HALLES, PARIS. **DECEMBER 18** TIVOLI, UTRECHT, HOLLAND. **DECEMBER 19** DOORNROOSJE, NIJMIEGEN, HOLLAND. **DECEMBER 21** PHILIPSHALLE, DUSSELDORF. **DECEMBER 22** MELKWEG, AMSTERDAM. **DECEMBER 30** LYCEUM, THE STRAND *WITH HANK WANGFORD BAND, FRANK CHICKENS.*

CONGRATULATIONS! YOU HAVE JUST PASSED THE B.B. SIGHT READING TEST. DID YOU SPOT THE DELIBERATE MISTAKE?

DISCOGRAPHY

LIFE'S A RIOT WITH SPY VS SPY

SIDE 1:

THE MILKMAN OF HUMAN KINDNESS,

TO HAVE AND TO HAVE NOT, RICHARD.

SIDE 2:

A NEW ENGLAND, THE MAN IN THE IRON MASK,

THE BUSY GIRL BUYS BEAUTY, LOVERS TOWN REVISITED.

GO! DISCS/UTILITY RECORDS: UTIL 1

BREWING UP WITH BILLY BRAGG

SIDE 1:

IT SAYS HERE, LOVE GETS DANGEROUS,

THE MYTH OF TRUST, FROM A VAUXHALL VELOX,

THE SATURDAY BOY, ISLAND OF NO RETURN.

SIDE 2:

ST. SWITHIN'S DAY, LIKE SOLDIERS DO,

THIS GUITAR SAYS SORRY, STRANGE THINGS HAPPEN,

A LOVER SINGS.

GO! DISCS: A GOLP 4

ADDITIONAL TRACKS ON COMPILATION LPs:

"A NEW OPTIMISM" *Situation Two Records SITU-11*

LP compiled by "Jamming" magazine, contains a specially

recorded version of "The Man In The Iron Mask"

featuring Dave Woodhead on flugelhorn. 1984

"LET THE CHILDREN PLAY" *Panic Records PEACE 1*

A double LP compiled in aid of peace camps in the U.K. Contains

a demo version of "Between the Wars." 1984

"DEPARTMENT OF ENJOYMENT" *Cassette only NMEO11*

Eleventh in a series of compilation tapes sold through the

New Musical Express. Contains a version of John Cale's

"Fear Is a Man's Best Friend."

BETWEEN THE WARS EP

SIDE 1:

BETWEEN THE WARS, WHICH SIDE ARE YOU ON.

SIDE 2:

THE WORLD TURNED UPSIDE DOWN, IT SAYS HERE.

GO! DISCS: A GOEP 1

EUROPEAN SINGLE

DOUBLE A SIDE:

ST. SWITHIN'S DAY, A NEW ENGLAND.

107 067 GERMANY 100; FRANCE/AE140

COVERS BY OTHERS

KIRSTY MacCOLL:

A NEW ENGLAND.

STIFF RECORDS: BUY 216

PAUL YOUNG:

"THE SECRET OF ASSOCIATION"

(CASSETTE ONLY)

THE MAN IN THE IRON MASK

CBS RECORDS: 4026234

RECOMMENDED BOOTLEGS

All of the following are available as bootleg cassettes.
Pay no more than £3.50 and make sure you hear
them first to check the quality.

NEW MERLIN'S CAVE 16/8/83

105 minutes of sharp patter and songs.

ICA ROCK WEEK 5/1/84

Fast and furious, Mr. Bragg denies he takes speed.

LYCEUM, LONDON 12/2/84

A sharp set sandwiched between The Redskins and The Smiths.

COLSTON HALL, BRISTOL 13/2/84

Billy Bragg opens for The Clash!

THE LONG WEEKEND

A handheld Walkman documentary recorded by the Rockin' Rad

himself and featuring live action from the
Trade Union Hall Watford 5/4/84, Acklam Hall 6/4/84 and
Bishop Douglas School East Finchley 7/4/84.

Nice one, Frank.

GLC JOBS FOR A CHANGE FESTIVAL 10/6/84

A ferocious set on that ferocious afternoon.

Also contains Ken Livingston's speech.

VICTORIA PALACE LONDON 27/10/84

Contains most of the set plus the encore with Hank Wangford Band
and Frank Chickens on "A13," "Fujiyama Mama" and "Green Banana."

If anyone has a tape of Billy's gig at
Nottingham Garage Club 22nd February 1984 please contact Go! Discs, Go!
Mansions, 8 Wendell Road, London W.12, (01) 743-3919 or 743-3845.

Billy would really like to hear it.

RADIO SESSIONS

FOR THE JOHN PEEL SHOW		St. Swithin's Day	FOR THE KID JENSEN SHOW
Recorded 27th July 1983	This Guitar Says Sorry	*Recorded 18th September 1984*	*Recorded 22nd December 1983*
A New England	A13, Trunk Road to the Sea	Which Side Are You On	Island of No Return
Love Gets Dangerous	*Recorded 21st February 1984*	Between the Wars	The Saturday Boy
Fear Is a Man's Best Friend	The Myth of Trust	It Says Here	Like Soldiers Do
Strange Things Happen	Lovers' Town	A Lover Sings	Man In the Iron Mask (& trumpet)
	To Have & Have Not		

It can be a very long walk between Euston Square tube station and Euston mainline station if you're carrying an amplifier, two guitars and a bag of clothes. If I've done it once this year, I've done it 20 times and I swear it's getting longer. ◇ Oh, the joys of being a pop star. I think my amp-carrying arm is getting longer too. I should swap arms sometimes but once you get a decent grip, it's better to keep moving, especially if you have a prevailing wind. White knuckles are the least of my problems, but rain *really* pisses me off. ◇ If you think life on the road is all private aircraft and limos or you cherish some romantic vision of seeing the world from a Transit van on the M62, let me show you another view in which no-one comes to pick you up in a limo or a Transit but you have to get a bus to the tube and then on to the station and then on to the gig. And so on. Then you come home and wash your socks and boil your hankies and start again. ◇ If you've never got past the bus stop at the end of the road then let me, dear reader, acquaint you with the bare necessities for rockin' all over the world:

1. A small amp. If you're going to lug the bastard thing all over the country on big bumpy trains, then I'm afraid the old Marshall Stack is right out of the window. ◇ Instead, you must go for something which is small but powerful. I have a Roland Cube 60 which is only 16 inches high but puts out BIG SOUND. If it's miked up it will easily fill the average club and will crank-up for big halls. I haven't tried it in any stadiums yet. It does tend to become a bit heavy after the first 800 yards but it's worth the hernia for the range of sounds. It retails at about £190 and will fit on the luggage rack of your average 125 Intercity Express.

2. Two guitars. I say two guitars because if you're playing solo and break a string you can become a lonely man with very big fingers as you try to re-string like a professional (NB: professionals have Roadies). I recently finished a gig in Leeds with only four strings intact. I told the audience that I was breaking all this metal because I wanted to be like Einsturzende Neubauten. I don't think they believed me. I use two Arbiter Les Paul TV copies. Sometimes I only take one, depends how lucky I feel.

3. Accoutrements: These are the little things that mean so much, like a toothbrush and an electric shaver so that you can do your ablutions in the lavvie as you whizz through Glossop at 125 mph. Firstly, you should have a big bag that goes over your shoulder to leave your hands free. In this should be your guitar leads, tuner, strings etc, stage clothes (if any) and a change of underpants. Underwear is very important. The ratio of days on the road to underpants should be 1:1. 3:1 is the minimum accepted by the Musicians Union and at anything above 7:1 you must be a member of King Kurt.

Other necessities are decent boots that don't leak, a couple of pairs of jeans (£6.50 each from High Street North, East Ham), a thick jumper (Oxfam should have some), a jacket that keeps out the rain, and a warm hat (both army surplus). Put all this gear on and you may look like the talking Action Man but at least you won't freeze to death in a bus shelter in Dundee waiting for Christmas or a bus. If you want to be really flash, you can buy yourself a flask for tea or Campari or whatever. ◇ You will require a modicum of agility and balance to carry all this gear. I suggest that you practice by loading yourself up and running up and down the stairs at Shepherds Bush tube station. Also needed is great patience, as anyone who regularly uses British Rail will realise. ◇ As far as sleeping arrangements go, it's a good idea to have strategically placed relatives and good friends in places like Edinburgh (Hi, Rosi), Manchester (Hello Bob) and Liverpool (love to Dot and Jane), otherwise anyone's sofa will do. Sleep is important and you should try and get some at least once a week. ◇ Be sure to take advantage of all BR's super-savers and stuff because it is very hard to run away from a ticket inspector whilst carrying an amp and two guitars. ◇ Before I got this job the furthest north I'd ever been was Catterick Garrison in Yorkshire but that's all changed now. My current ambition is to do a gig in Kirkwall on the Orkney Isles. I'm really looking forward to that. There's also a possibility of going to America

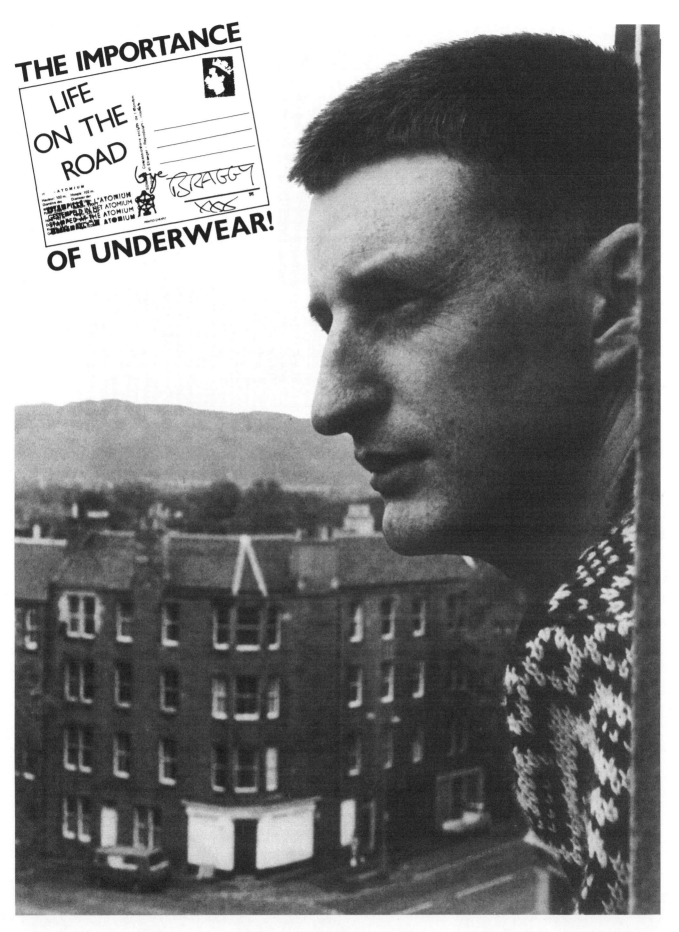

THE IMPORTANCE

LIFE
ON THE
ROAD

OF UNDERWEAR!

but if that doesn't work out, well sod it, it's only a hobby. ◇ Chances are in the next twelve months I'll be coming to your town, playing your burgh, but in the meantime if you're sitting on a 125 opposite a bloke with a big nose and a funny hat and the train lurches and a guitar falls on your head, don't be too harsh on him. It's probably me.

First published December 24th 1983. Reproduced, courtesy of Sounds.

LIFE LONG FRIEND FORMER RIFF RAFF STALWART & STAGE FAVORITE WIGGY REVEALS.. "I TAUGHT HIM EVERYTHING"

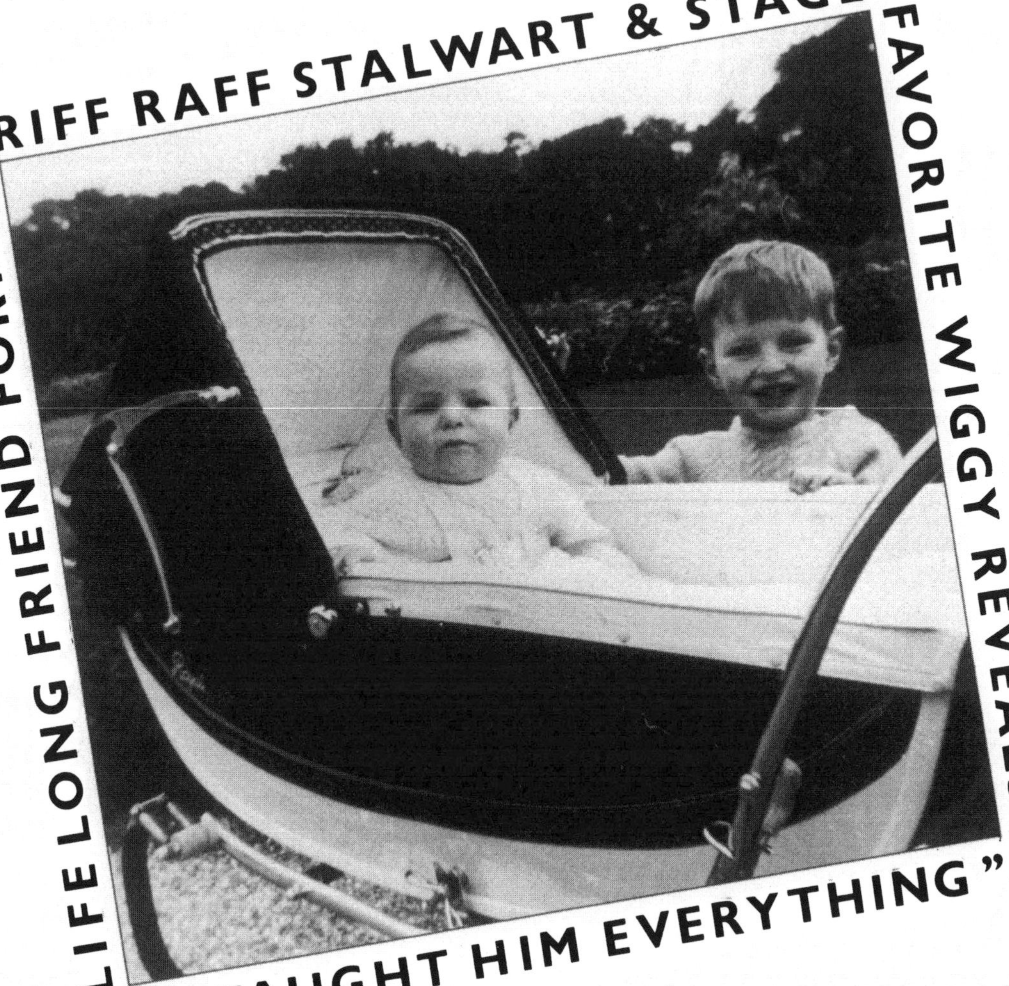

1960 Infamous photosession with me & Billy in Barking Park. **1966** Billy breaks the front wheel off my Thunderbird 1. ▷ **1969** Subbuteo disaster. Many players crushed under runaway dartboard. ▷ **1971** Bragg discovers that I have a record player and a few Thunderbirds albums and 'Maggie May' to play on it. He decides to enlarge my musical experience while pursuing his own desire to hear some of the records he'd bought in anticipation of owning his own deck some day. ▷ **1972** Bragg joins the line up of Guy Norris Ltd. as a Saturday Boy in the hardware department in an effort to get even more vinyl from their record basement to play on my record player. ▷ **1974** Bragg learns that I am a budding Ron Wood and gets me to teach him how to play guitar. During the next few months far too many 'one minute wonders' emerged from the Wigg/Bragg songwriting school. ▷ **1975** We take co-ownership in a Selmer twin 30 zodiac combo, with one speaker missing and some terrifying acoustic habits. Billy also buys various cheesecutter type electric guitars and we proceed in the traditional rock 'n' roll starting ground-Backrooms! With the welcome addition of Mr R Handley on drums. ▷ **1976** By now too loud for backrooms we took several 16 hour block bookings at local rehearsal rooms. ▷ Saw the Stones at Earls Court

RIFF RAFF LINE-UP FROM THE 'COSMONAUT' EP 1978

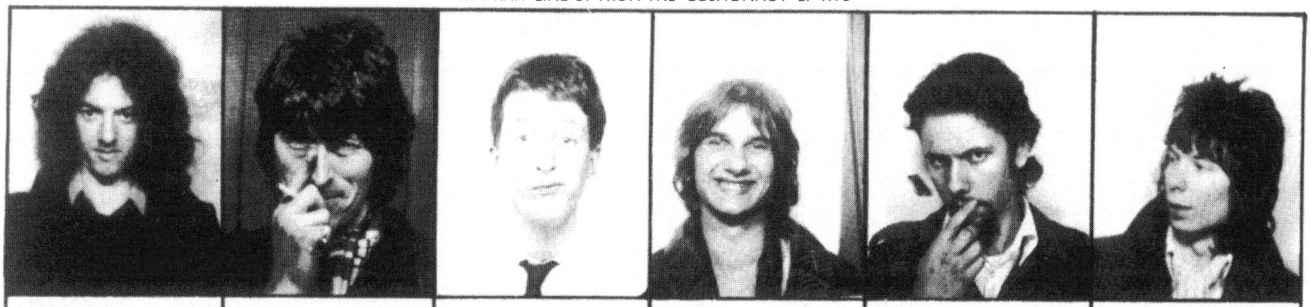

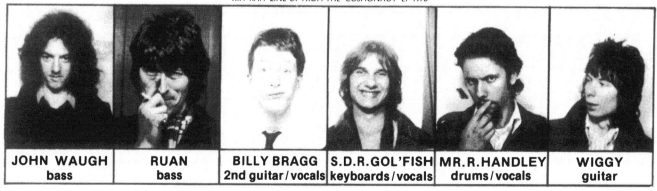

JOHN WAUGH	RUAN	BILLY BRAGG	S.D.R.GOL'FISH	MR.R.HANDLEY	WIGGY
bass	bass	2nd guitar / vocals	keyboards / vocals	drums / vocals	guitar

KEEF, ER, WOODY, ER, JONESY, ER, WIGGY

from the front row and had our lives changed. ▷ Also, first gig for the as yet unnamed and bass player-less Riff Raff at a talent contest at the Queen's Theatre, Hornchurch. Paid £5 to play for 8 minutes, and along with Iron Maiden got beaten by a 14 year old Carlos Santana by the name of Duggie Boyle. ▷ **1977** Now with more money than sense (coz we all 'ad day jobs) Riff Raff Mk. I took a holiday in the form of a one week block booking at a rehearsal studio where we wrote and demo-ed Romford Girls. ▷ Saw the Clash at the Rainbow. Lives changed again. ▷ First London gigs, at the Red Cow, Hammersmith, we were approached by Chiswick records to record a one off EP. ▷ **1978** JANUARY EP finally recorded. More gigs at the classic London pub venues plus assorted Barn dances and Dentists' Dinners. ▷ APRIL We all move to Oundle nr. Peterborough to rehearse, write, record, play, stay up late, meet schoolgirls etc, etc, etc. ▷ MAY Played on top of a local pile of shit for BBC's That's Life. Also this period was the start of the dreaded longterm residency at the Red Lion, Clopton. ▷ **1978** JULY EP released to rave reviews: "Riff Raff, 'I Want to be a Cosmonaut.' I wish he would and take his record with him." *Melody Maker.* ▷ NOVEMBER Four bass players later, Riff Raff take up residence in "Wobbling Heights." A one up, one

THOSE ILL-ADVISED RIFF RAFF SLEEVES

IT SEEMED LIKE A GOOD IDEA AT THE TIME

YET ANOTHER RIFF RAFF LINE-UP 1980

down, and one further up, 18 inches from the A605.. (Whilst juggernauts thundered by) the bog came away from the drain pipe, the plastic sink got pulled off the wall. We all slept in the same room, up to twenty or so at times, sardine fashion. You'd wake up to find strangers eating the last two turkey eggs and you had to use a teaspoon to get out of the front door. . . ▷ **1980** More of the same until we decided in our infinite wisdom to release four singles and a video simultaneously on our own label "Geezer Records." Riff Raff was in a state of flux as usual but we managed to find a deaf keyboard player and a drummer who was 12 years old, and went in to record. ▷ SEPTEMBER Reformed again and with Riff Raff MkVIII. Quickly played the last of the London rock venues before they all burnt down or turned into wine bars.   **1981** EARLY.. Billy got his call up papers and our fifth bass player got bored! I went and told the drummer "It's all over," the rest is history. . . . . . .

Errors and omissions are to be expected. . . .

SONG INDEX

33

LIKE SOLDIERS DO

35

PORKYS' ILLUSTRATION FOR

36

STRANGE THINGS HAPPEN.

38

A LOVER SINGS

40

IT SAYS HERE

42

THE MYTH OF TRUST

44

ISLAND OF NO RETURN

46

RICHARD

49

FROM A VAUXHALL VELOX

51

THE SATURDAY BOY

54

A NEW ENGLAND

56

THE BUSY GIRL BUYS BEAUTY

58

THE MILKMAN OF HUMAN KINDNESS

60

THE MAN IN THE IRON MASK

62

TO HAVE AND TO HAVE NOT

63

PORKY'S ILLUSTRATION FOR

64

LOVERS TOWN REVISITED.

65

ST SWITHIN'S DAY

66

BETWEEN THE WARS

68

LOVE GETS DANGEROUS

69

THIS GUITAR SAYS SORRY

ALL SONGS WRITTEN BY BILLY BRAGG

REPRODUCED BY PERMISSION OF CHAPPELL MUSIC LTD.

12 FRET NECK MAP

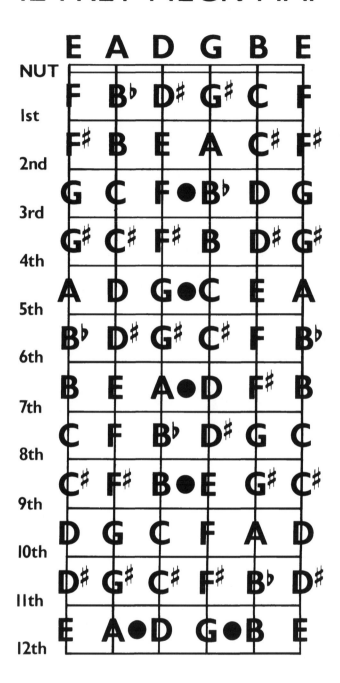

FOR USE WITH THE BACK TO BASICS AUDIO AID.

USELESS AFTER THE FIRST 10,000 COPIES.

LIKE SOLDIERS DO

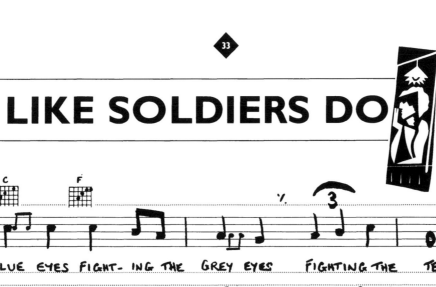

(1.3.) BLUE EYES FIGHT-ING THE GREY EYES FIGHTING THE TEARS
(2.) NOTHING IS CLEAR IN THIS TACTICAL UN- CLEAR WAR

ARMED TO THE TEETH FOR A WAR OF WORDS_ REACH-ING
I CAN'T BE BOTH-ERED TO FIND OUT WHAT_ WE'RE

ALL THE YEARS_ I AD- VANCED ACROSS A POPPY FIELD_
FIGHT-ING FOR._ NO ONE CAN WIN THIS WAR OF THE

to Coda

I SAW THE GLEAM AS YOU RAISED YOUR SHIELD AND
SEN- SES_ I SEE NO REASON TO DROP MY DE- FENCES SO

LOVE SCREAMED DOWN WITH THE SUN_ BE- HIND_ ITS BACK_
STAND FAST MY EMOTIONS RALLY ROUND MY SHAK-ING HEART._

OUR FATHERS WERE ALL SOLD-IERS, SHALL

WE BE SOLD-IERS TOO, FIGHT-ING AND

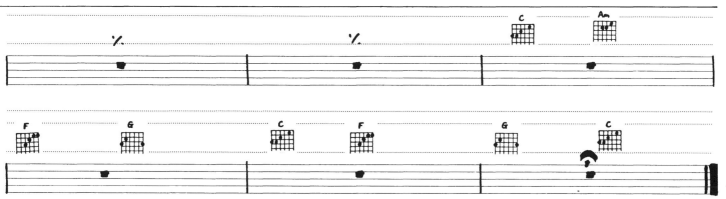

STRANGE THINGS HAPPEN

RPT. TO FADE

A LOVER sings

IT SAYS HERE

REPEAT TO FADE

THE MYTH OF TRUST

I WOKE UP THIS MORN-ING TO FIND THAT WE HAD OUT-LIVED THE MYTH OF TRUST.

FINE

YOU WOKE UP THIS MORN-ING TO THE FACT WE'VE LOST THE THINGS WE TOOK FOR GRANTED BETWEEN US.

BECAUSE I GREW UP IN AWE OF THE GIRL NEXT DOOR AND THE BOY THAT NEV-ER CRIED. I WAS DREAMING OF THOSE EL--IZABETHAN GIRLS WHILE YOU WERE WORKING IN THE MARK-ET TO EARN OUR-SELVES AND WHEN YOU FOUND OUT WHAT HAPPENED YESTERDAY WHILE YOU WERE AWAY IN THIS

ISLAND OF NO RETURN

RICHARD

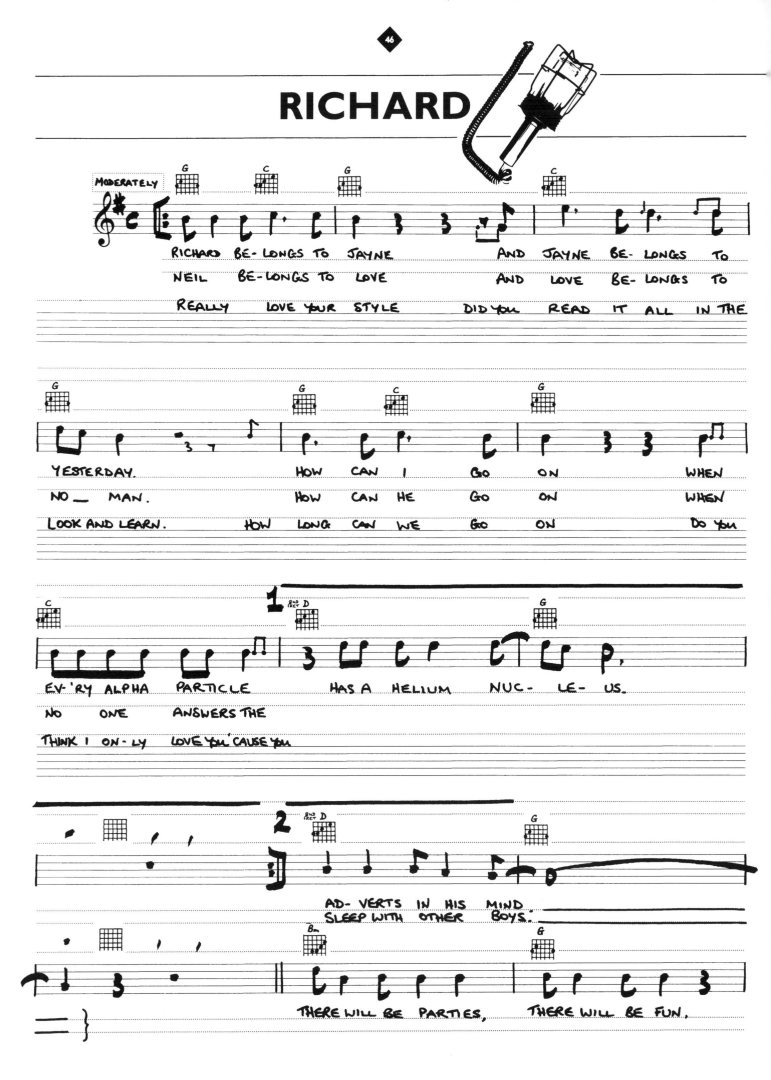

HEY   HEY ____   HEY,   HERE COMES   RICHARD,

HEY, HERE COMES

N.B.

RICH-   ARD _____

FROM A VAUXHALL VELOX

SHE SAID, DO THESE SEATS FOLD DOWN?   AND I SAID, ____ IF YOU

HER MO- THER   READ HER MAIL   AND HER

SOME PEOPLE SAY   LOVE IS BLIND   BUT I. THINK THAT THAT'S A

PULL THAT HAND- LE _____

DAD WAS A POL- ICE- MAN _____

BIT SHORT- SIGHT- ED. _____

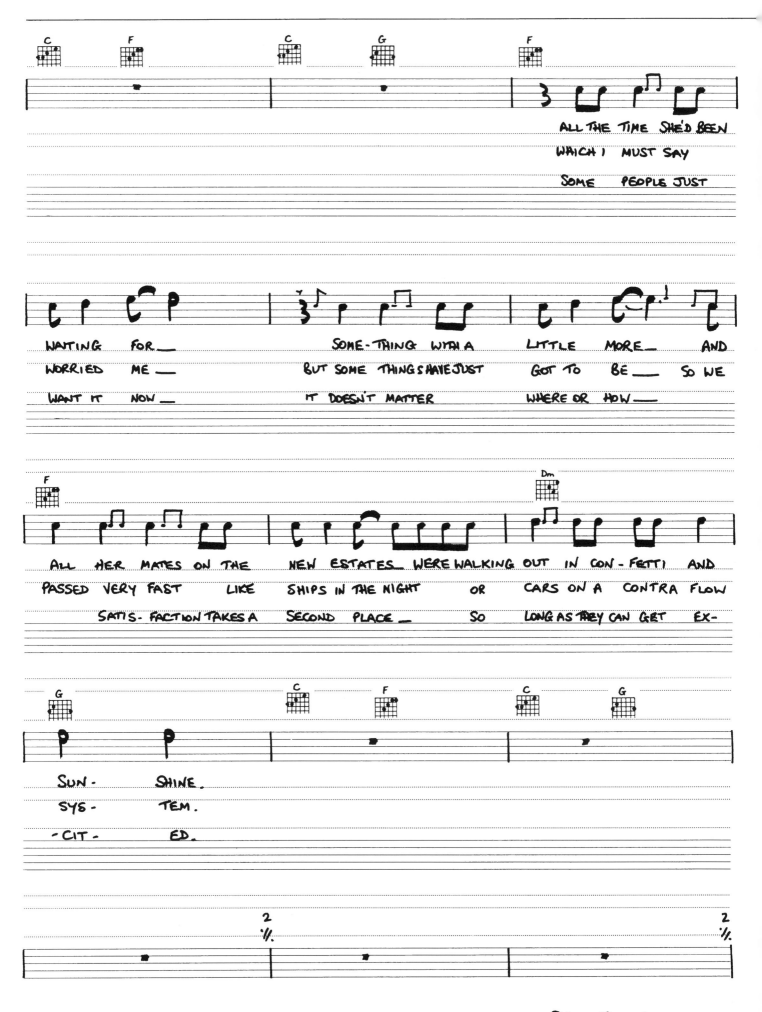

3° - FADE

THE SATURDAY BOY

I'LL NEVER FORGET THE FIRST DAY I MET HER

THAT SEPT-EMBER MORN-ING WAS CLEAR AND FRESH. THE WAY SHE SPOKE AND

LAUGHED AT MY JOKES AND THE WAY SHE RUBBED HER-SELF AGAINST THE EDGE OF MY DESK.

SHE BE-CAME A MAGIC MYSTERY TO ME AND WE'D SIT TO-GETHER IN DOUBLE

HISTORY ONCE A WEEK AND SOME DAYS WE'D WALK THE SAME WAY HOME, AND IT'S SURPRIS-

-ING HOW QUICK A LITTLE RAIN CAN CLEAR THE STREETS. WE DREAMED OF HER AND COM-

-PARED OUR DREAMS, BUT THAT WAS ALL THAT I EV-ER TAST-ED

SHE LIED TO ME WITH HER BODY YOU SEE, AND I LIED TO MY-SELF 'BOUT THE

IN THE END IT TOOK ME A DICT - ION - ARY, TO FIND OUT THE MEANING OF

UN - RE - QUIT - ED LOVE. ___ WHILE SHE WAS GIVING HER - SELF FOR FREE AT A

PARTY TO WHICH I WAS NEVER IN - VIT - ED. I NEVER UNDER - STOOD MY

FAIL - INGS THEN AND I HIDE MY HUMBLE HOPES NOW.

(Spoken) THINKING BACK, SHE MADE US WANT HER, A GIRL NOT OLD E - NOUGH TO SHAVE HER

LEGS. ___ (Trumpet)

AD LIB, TO FADE

A NEW ENGLAND

FAST BEAT

I WAS TWENTY ONE YEARS WHEN I WROTE THIS SONG, I'M
LOVED YOU THEN AS I LOVE YOU STILL, THOUGH I
LOVED THE WORDS YOU WROTE TO ME BUT
SAW TWO SHOOT-ING STARS LAST NIGHT, I

TWENTY TWO NOW BUT I WON'T BE FOR LONG, PEOPLE ASK ME WHEN WILL YOU GROW
PUT YOU ON A PEDESTAL, THEY PUT YOU ON THE PILL. I DON'T FEEL BAD A-BOUT
THAT WAS BLOOD-Y YEST-ER-DAY. I CAN'T SUR-VIVE ON
WISHED ON THEM BUT THEY WERE ONLY SATELLITES, IS IT WRONG TO WISH ON

UP TO BE A MAN BUT ALL THE GIRLS I LOVED AT SCHOOL ARE AL-READY PUSHING PRAMS.
LETTING YOU GO, I JUST FEEL SAD A-BOUT LETTING YOU KNOW.
WHAT YOU SEND, EV-'RY TIME YOU NEED A FRIEND.
SPACE HARD-WARE, I WISH, I WISH I WISH YOU'D CARE.

THE BUSY GIRL BUYS BEAUTY

THE BUS-Y GIRL BUYS BEAU-TY

THE PRETTY GIRL BUYS

STYLE. AND THE SIMPLE GIRL

BUYS WHAT SHE'S TOLD TO BUY

AND SEES HER WORLD THROUGH THE BRIGHTLY LIT EYES OF THE

GLOSSY ROMANCE OF FASH-ION. WHERE SHE CAN LEARN

TOP TIPS FOR THE GAS COOK SUCCESSFUL SECRETS OF A

SEXUAL KIND, THE DAILY DRILL FOR BEAUTIFUL HAIR

(RPT. TO FADE)

THE MILKMAN OF HUMAN KINDNESS

IF YOU'RE LONE-LY ... I WILL CALL
IF YOU'RE SLEEP-ING ... I WILL WAIT
IF YOU'RE FALL-ING ... I'LL PUT OUT MY HANDS

IF YOU'RE POOR-LY
IF YOUR BED IS WET
IF YOU FEEL BITTER

I WILL SEND PO-ET-RY.
I WILL DRY YOUR TEARS.
I WILL UND-ER-STAND.

I LOVE YOU, I AM THE

MILKMAN OF HUMAN KIND-NESS, I WILL LEAVE AN EX-TRA

THE MAN IN THE IRON MASK

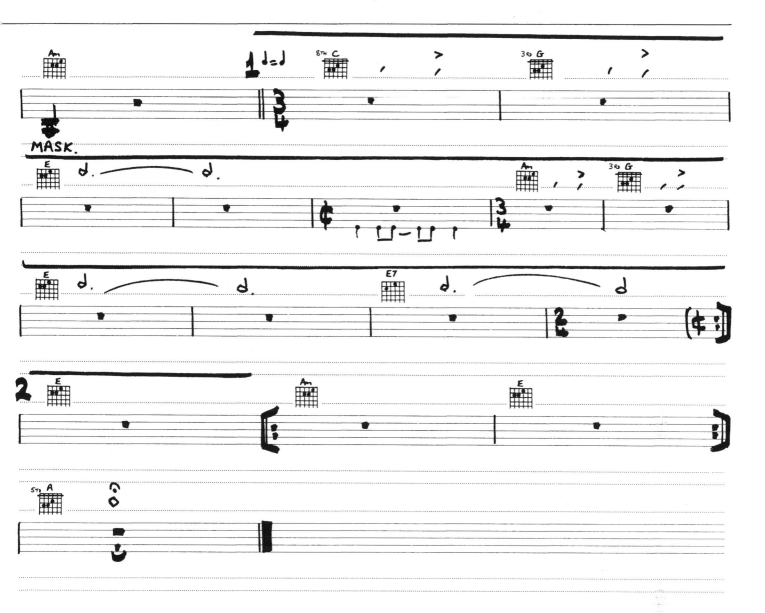

VERSE 2

YOU SAID YOU LOVED ME AND IT BROKE MY HEART
I WAS ALWAYS YOUR PRISONER, RIGHT FROM THE START.
THE NIGHTS YOU SPEND WITHOUT ME,
THIS HOUSE IS LIKE A DUNGEON
AND YOU ONLY RETURN TO TORTURE ME MORE.
YOU MUST HAVE YOUR REASONS, I WILL NOT ASK,
FOR YOU, I WILL BE THE MAN IN THE IRON MASK.

TO HAVE AND TO HAVE NOT

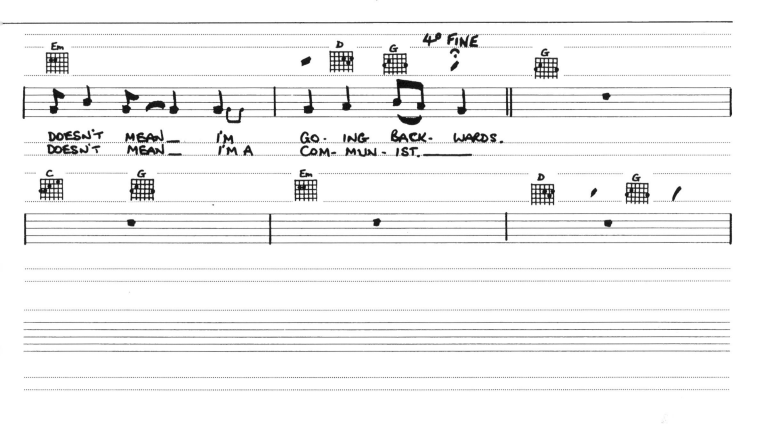

DOESN'T MEAN_ I'M GO-ING BACK-WARDS.
DOESN'T MEAN_ I'M A COM-MUN-IST.___

LOVERS TOWN REVISITED

LOVERS TOWN REVISITED

STOP AND THINK. { SOMETIMES_ IT MAKES ME TURN AWAY ___ SOME-
{ BUT MOST TIMES_ IT MAKES ME RUN A - WAY.

ST. SWITHIN'S DAY

THINKING BACK   NOW___   I SUP-POSE
HANDS___   WHEN I MAKE
SAME___   BUT I JUST CAN'T

YOU WERE JUST STATING YOUR   VIEWS, WHAT WAS IT ALL   FOR___
LOVE TO YOUR   MEMORY   IT'S NOT THE   SAME___
BRING MY-SELF TO ANSWER YOUR   LETTERS, IT'S NOT YOUR   FAULT___

FOR THE WEATH- ER OR THE BATTLE OF AG- IN COURT,_ AND THE TIMES_
I MISS THE THUNDER,__   I MISS THE RAIN,____ AND THE FACT_
BUT YOUR HON- EST-Y TOUCH-ES ME LIKE A FIRE,____ THE POLAR-

| C/F | Em-9 | Em |

THAT WE ALL HOPED WOULD LAST, LIKE A TRAIN THEY HAVE GONE BY SO FAST

THAT YOU DON'T UNDER- STAND. CASTS A SHAD- OW OV- ER THIS LAND

-OIDS THAT HOLD US TO- GETH-ER, WILL SURE- LY FADE A-WAY

| Am7 | C/F | C | Gb add 4 |

AND THOUGH WE STOOD TOGETH- ER ON THE EDGE OF THE PLAT- FORM, WE WERE NOT MOVED

BUT THE SUN STILL SHINES FROM BEHIND

LIKE THE LOVE THAT WE SPOKE OF FOR- EV- ER ON SAINT SWITH-

| C/F | C | C/D | Gb add 4 | 1,2 |

BRIDGE

BY THEM. WITH MY OWN

IT. THANKS ALL THE

-INS DAY.

3

INSTRUMENTAL

TO FADE

BETWEEN THE WARS

| G | Am | C | G | D | Em |

I WAS A MINER, I WAS A DOCK- ER, I WAS A RAILWAYMAN BE-

I KEPT THE FAITH AND I KEPT VOT- ING, NOT FOR THE IRON FIST BUT

CALL UP THE CRAFTSMEN, BRING ME THE DRAUGHTS-MEN, BUILD ME A PATH FROM

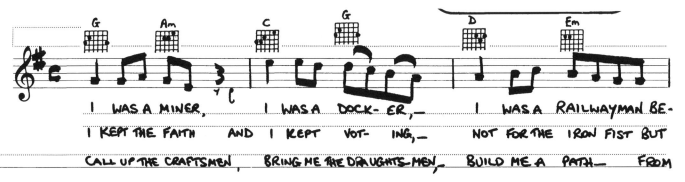

LOVE GETS DANGEROUS

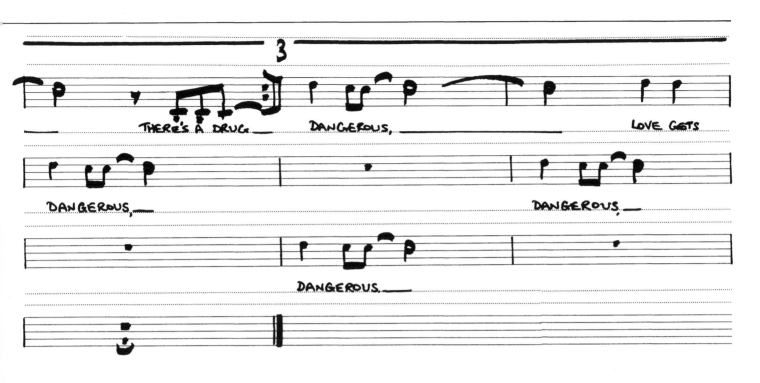

THERE'S A DRUG... DANGEROUS, _____ LOVE GETS

DANGEROUS, ___ DANGEROUS,_

DANGEROUS._

THIS GUITAR SAYS SORRY

SANDRA MET RAYMOND AT THE RACE RE-LA-TIONS___
TIME THAT IT TAKES TO MAKE A BA-BY____
STILL GOES DANCING AND SHE STILL CUTS HAIR____

MUCH TO THE DIS-MAY OF HER FAMILY AND FRIENDS.___
CAN BE THE TIME IT TAKES_ TO MAKE A CUP OF TEA. ___
THEY PUT THE BA-BY IN-TO COUN-CIL CARE.___

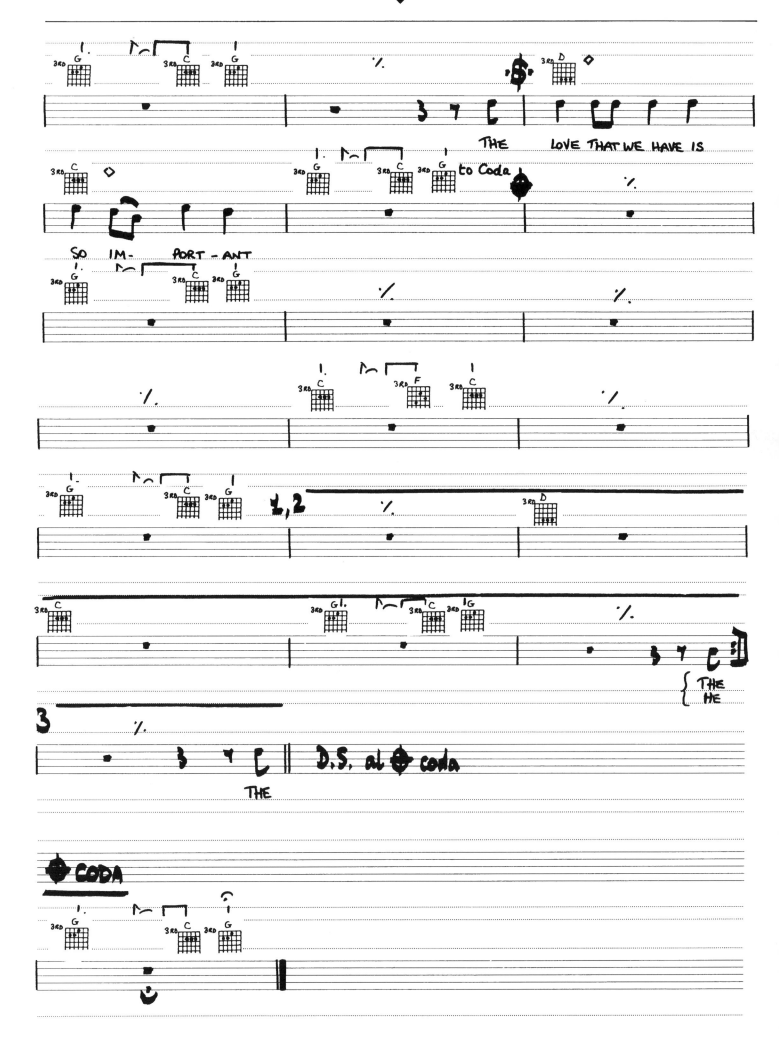

PHOTOGRAPHY CREDITS

BACK COVER BOB BROMIDE

PG. 1 ERIC WATSON PG. 2 BOB BROMIDE

PG. 4 ANDY KERSHAW PG. 6 JAYNE

PG. 7 CAROLE SEGAL PG. 8/9 PENNIE SMITH

PG. 13 LAURIE SPARHAM PG. 14 PAUL RIDER

PG. 15 WIGGY . PG. 16 ANDY KERSHAW

PG. 17 (LEFT) JACKIE MACKAY (RIGHT) KEN COPSEY

PG. 18 MICK PEAK FROM A KEVIN CUMMINS PHOTO

PG. 19 NIKKI RODGERSON PG. 20 (LEFT)

NIKKI RODGERSON (RIGHT) PAUL SLATTERY

PG. 21 ANDY KERSHAW (SPOT THE ONE BY BILLY)

PG. 22 (TOP) NIKKI RODGERSON (MIDDLE) PAUL

SLATTERY (BOTTOM) PETER JENNER

PG. 23 PAUL SLATTERY PG. 24 ANDY KERSHAW

PG. 25 NIKKI RODGERSON PG. 27 ANDY KERSHAW

PG. 28 POSSIBLY WIGGY'S MUM

PG. 29 ANDY KERSHAW PG. 72 PAUL SLATTERY

MUSIC TRANSCRIBED AND PREPARED BY ROGER DAY

PRINTED IN ENGLAND

TYPESET IN GILL SANS BY TOM HAND

DESIGN & COWGUM - CARAMEL/CRUNCH DESIGN

MAKE IT YOUR PARTY

POLITICS IS ABOUT CHOICE

It's about deciding
what sort of world we
want to live in
About whether we want
to see a whole generation
go to waste on the dole
Or whether we want
a government that will
work together with
the people of Britain to
invest in industry
and jobs for the future
Put like that the
choice is clear
Labour is the party of the
working people and Labour
is the party that will
get people back to work

**IF LABOUR IS
YOUR CHOICE
MAKE LABOUR
YOUR PARTY**

**TOGETHER
WE WILL BUILD
A BETTER FUTURE
FOR US ALL**

PLEASE FILL OUT THE COUPON AND RETURN (NO STAMP NEEDED) TO,

☐ I WOULD LIKE TO KNOW MORE ABOUT THE LABOUR PARTY

☐ I WOULD LIKE TO JOIN THE LABOUR PARTY

☐ I ENCLOSE A DONATION (PAYABLE TO THE LABOUR PARTY)

NAME _____

ADDRESS_____

_____ POST CODE_____

THE LABOUR PARTY

FREEPOST, LONDON SE17 IBR.